HANDICRAFTS FOR Holidays

By Janet and Alex D'Amato

Foreword by Morton Thompson, Ed. D.

THE LION PRESS

Publishers, New York

© 1967 by The Lion Press, Inc., 274 Madison Avenue, New York, New York
Published simultaneously in Canada by George J. McLeod, Ltd.
73 Bathurst Street, Toronto 2B, Ontario
This book printed and bound in the United States of America by
American Book-Stratford Press
Library of Congress No. 67-27108
Second Printing

Table of Contents

Foreword

Here is an exciting book for children ages 7-12; a book loaded with suggestions for creative ideas related to major holidays throughout the year. The book details easy-to-make projects, which when completed, are sturdy and attractive as well as functional for the particular holiday concerned. Holidays involved include Valentine's day, Easter, Columbus day, Halloween and Christmas.

To begin with, the authors suggest the collection of a variety of items found around the house, which can be utilized to produce many of the wonderful projects in this book. Some of these items are egg cartons, glue, plastic bottles, disposable foil plates, paint and cardboard tubes found inside wax paper or bathroom tissue. The book describes a number of projects for each holiday. These run the gamut from Valentine and Christmas cards to a variety of games, mobiles, hats and gifts.

The book is extremely interesting as well as practical since it can be used during every season of the year. Furthermore, it provides plenty of suggestions that may well motivate young readers to create additional ideas and projects of their own.

Such a book will guide children in the exercise of basic handicraft skills and assist them in the development of imagination and creativity as related to structure, pattern and design.

Handicrafts For Holidays should make a valuable addition to every library and agency concerned with the interests of children and should serve as an excellent resource guide for teachers, parents, recreation leaders, camp counselors and others interested in the educational needs of children.

We enthusiastically recommend this book.

Morton Thompson Ed. D.
Recreation Consultant
Recreational Research Institute

Introduction

Hello! We have planned activities and projects that you can make on different holidays of the year. Most of them are made from ordinary everyday objects that you can find around your house. None require any special art, talent or skill, but they do require patience and imagination. Use our ideas as starters but please feel free to change materials, colors or add more decorations.

Treasure Box of Valuable Trash: Use a corrugated box to stash away anything you feel might come in handy on these projects—bits of old jewelry, shells, buttons, pine cones, feathers, berry boxes, yarn and fabric scraps, etc. Interesting trim will add magic to your homemade items. You will also need scissors, paste, glue, crepe paper, poster paints, pipe cleaners, soda straws, staples, transparent sticky tape and a paper punch.

Molded Egg Cartons: These provide a source of ready-made paper maché. Cut the desired shape and soak in warm water for an hour. Shape as desired, dry and then color as directed. Supermarket meat and fruit trays are made of the same material.

Cardboard Tubes: You'll find them inside rolls of wax paper and foil (12″) mailing tubes (all sizes), or bathroom tissue (4″).

Plastic Bottles: Bleach and liquid soap or other laundry liquids come in these bottles. Wash, remove labels and dry. Before cutting, fill with hot water for about 10 minutes; then pour the water out. Hot water softens the plastic for easier cutting. A small sharp knife is best to start; continue with large scissors. An awl or nail is used to make holes. Ask your Dad to help you on this. Once cut, you can do the rest yourself.

Disposable Aluminum Foil Plates: Various pies, cakes and frozen dishes come in these. They can be cut with scissors. Although the edges are not too sharp, we do recommend using caution in handling the cut edges. Sometimes paper plates can be substituted.

Vinyl Adhesive-Backed Plastic: This can be purchased at your local hardware store if you don't have scraps around. It comes in a variety of colors and textures. To use, peel off the paper backing. It's a useful covering when glue and paint won't stick (on certain plastic surfaces). There are also colored tapes. If you prefer, colored construction paper pasted on is a substitute. However, the vinyl surface gives a much more permanent finish.

Felt-Tipped Pens: These markers come in a variety of colors. They will color or decorate many surfaces that will not take paint or crayons.

Glue: There are two types, and when necessary we have told you which to use. Household cement comes in tubes and is transparent. This holds better on smooth surfaces. White glue comes in a plastic bottle and is good for most general purposes. For paper and cardboard, you may use paste.

Spray Paint: This should be handled with care and with your parents' help. Put whatever you are spraying inside a large box or outdoors on newspaper.

Hints in General: Whenever there is a pattern given, lay a lightweight piece of paper over it that enables you to see the lines. Trace the pattern; then transfer it with carbon paper to whatever you are going to cut. *Don't cut the book.*

Never use any materials until they are ready to be thrown out or your parents have given their permission. (Glance through the book and get an idea of the materials you'll be using before anything you need is thrown out.)

As each holiday comes along, you'll find interesting and attractive things to make. And whether you have a party or not, its fun to create your own table decorations which make any dinner a holiday occasion. So create and have fun making treasured gifts for family and friends out of homely household castoffs. Here's to many happy, busy holidays!

New Year Memory Scrapbook

Cut two pieces of fairly heavy cardboard 10″ x 5″. Cover them with attractive paper. Then collect a dozen legal-size envelopes (4″ x 9½″) and trim the flaps, as shown. Next, cut out the names of the months of the year from an old calendar or one your parents don't need. Paste the name of a different month on each envelope and decorate appropriately. Punch holes 1″ in from both corners on the left hand sides of the envelopes. Mark matching holes in the cardboard covers, and punch out. Tie everything together with a ribbon and put the year and your name on the cover.

From now on, whenever there is an item about someone you know in your school paper, you can save it, as well as other clippings or snapshots or mementos. Slip them in the envelope each month. At the end of the year, you will have a delightful record of good times to look back on.

A Perky Hat

Use a 10″ tin-foil plate or a colorful paper plate. Cut out the center flat area. Cut a piece of crepe paper about 20″ long and 10″ wide. Tape it to the inside of the cut outer edge with small pieces of tape.

For the pompom on top, cut a 4″ x 10″ piece from a roll of aluminum foil. Cut slits partway down, as shown. Then roll up and slip inside the top. Gather the crepe paper and foil, and hold with a rubber band. Twist out the paper and foil strips to look festive. Use a 1″ x 20″ strip of ribbon or crepe paper to cover the cut edge of the plate on outside. Tape it at 3″ intervals with transparent tape.

Rubber Band

6

New Year Noisemaker

Use large cardboard spools from gift-wrapping ribbon. (There are probably several around the house left over from the holidays.) Either the flat type or the taller one can be used. Trace around both the ends on colored paper and cut out the two units. Paste the first side onto the spool. Then drop some dried peas or gravel into the other hole and cover the second side with your other colored paper circle. Decorate the middle with ribbon or bright paper.

Push an unsharpened pencil through the center holes until it sticks out about ½″ on the top. Secure it with transparent tape. Cut a piece of string or ribbon about 12″ long. Tie a jingle bell on each end, and tie the ribbon around the pencil top, as shown. Tape, so it won't slide off. Now shake, rattle and have a party with your noisemaker.

Valentine Heartful Centerpiece

Select a cardboard box for your centerpiece. Something around 6″ x 10″ would be fine, or larger if you are having a big party. Your box should be 4″ to 5″ high. Cover it with red paper. Draw triangle shapes opposite each other in the center of the long sides of your box. Cut out the two triangles. Cut out six red hearts. Glue each to a small white paper doilie. Cut other doilie in half and glue inside the top of the box, to peak out and give a lacy valentine look. Glue hearts to box.

Count the number of **guests** you plan to have. Wrap a tiny present in red or white tissue paper for each. The presents should be small enough to fit through your cut-out triangles. Tie each gift with a red ribbon. Be sure to leave one end of the ribbon about 20″ long. Cut out two small hearts and glue back to back at the end of each ribbon (see picture).

Place the gifts in the box and pull the ribbons out through the triangles. Tape a crisscross the red ribbon over the top of the box with loops at the corners.

When your guests are ready, each chooses a ribbon and gently pulls his or her gift out of the box. This makes a pretty table centerpiece. And who doesn't like a surprise party present!

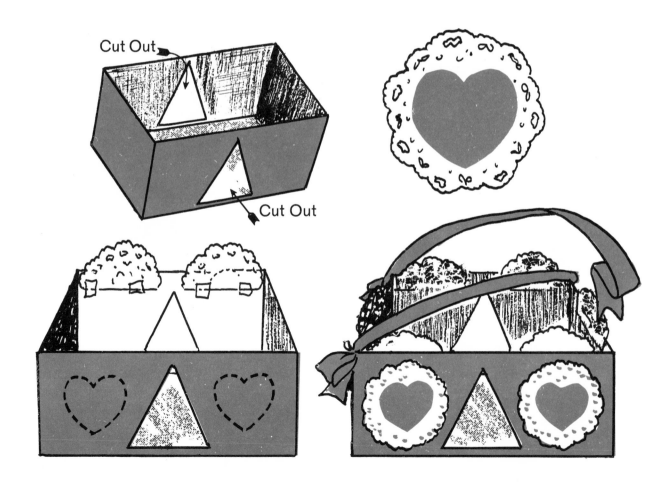

Pattern for
hearts on
ribbon

A Heart Mobile

Mark off a spiral on the back of a 10″ heavy foil plate. Start just inside the rim and follow that edge almost all the way around. Spiral into the center, with about 1″ between the lines, as shown by the colored line. Cut along the line you have drawn, leaving the rim intact.

Wind the rim with red yarn, letting the silver show. Tie at point A. Bring one strand of the yarn up through the spiral to the center, point B. Hold it up so that it makes the desired spiral shape. Then tie at the top and make a hanging loop above. Paste on small red hearts, or color them on with red felt-tipped markers.

Using pattern below, trace off half heart and draw other half. Cut two hearts out of heavy red paper. Cut slits as shown and slip together. Tie at the top with thread and continue the thread up to top of the spiral and tie. Using colored pattern below, trace and cut out smaller hearts, tie with thread and hang from the rim. Then watch your hearts dance.

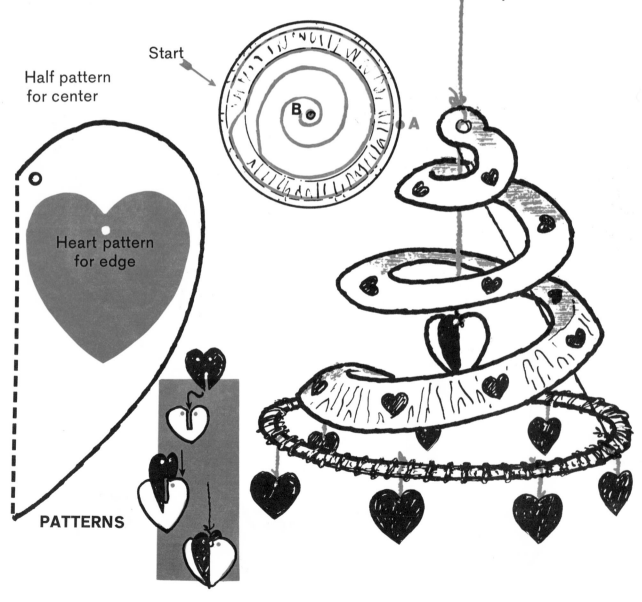

Start

Half pattern
for center

Heart pattern
for edge

PATTERNS

10

A Valentine Reflection

Make this valentine for someone very special. *Don't mail it*. Use an old pocketbook mirror, or buy one in a dime store. Cut two pieces of heavy white paper 4″ x 6½″, or large enough to cover your mirror. Cut a circle 2½″ in diameter on one piece. Tape your mirror on the other piece. Put paste around the mirror and put the cut-out front over it so the mirror is under the hole. Clip some clothespins around the sides to hold until dry.

Using the heart in the picture for a pattern, cut a valentine shape of red paper. Then cut it down the middle. When the mirror back is dry, place your heart over the circle and tape the two outside edges so the heart can be opened. Then letter your message and decorate your card.

Valentines 4—U—2 Make

Rebus cards are fun to do. Numbers can be taken from last month's calendar page. Pictures and letters can be found in old magazines. Look for big lettered headlines in ads to get a "C" or "U" or whatever you need. And a large photo of a face can be cut so you get just one eye.

Use flat or folded cards of red or white paper. Plan them to fit envelopes you already have. Arrange and paste in place. Letter in any words you need, as shown.

The "rope" is a piece of string glued on and continued through to the inside of a folded card. It is caught under the red heart valentine.

String

Inside

AM 4

Inside

BE MINE

A good rule

Inside

Ruler

Inside

Picture of a can

U C me

4 your

Inside

12

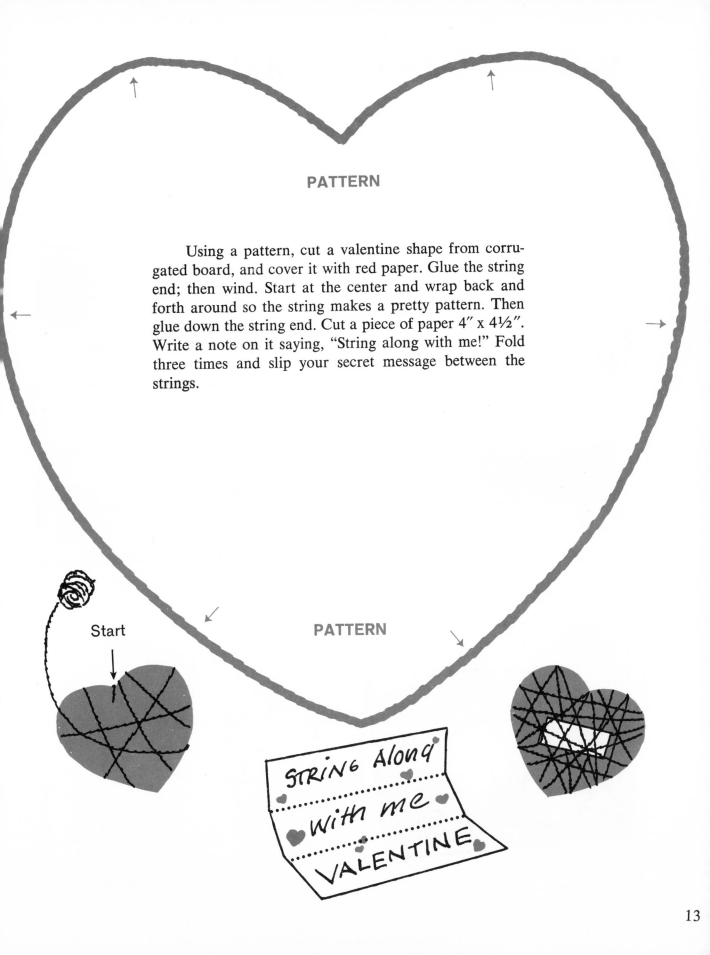

PATTERN

Using a pattern, cut a valentine shape from corrugated board, and cover it with red paper. Glue the string end; then wind. Start at the center and wrap back and forth around so the string makes a pretty pattern. Then glue down the string end. Cut a piece of paper 4″ x 4½″. Write a note on it saying, "String along with me!" Fold three times and slip your secret message between the strings.

Start

PATTERN

STRING Along with me VALENTINE

Penny-Wise Place Cards

To make these Lincoln penny personal place cards, cut a piece of heavy construction paper 7½″ x 3¾″. Use pennies as part of the design. Trace around the pennies. Then draw the rest of the design and color it. Letter in the name you want and glue the pennies in place. Fold the card and paste the two bases together, making a standing triangle or tent. Your friends will be delighted by your penny-wise place cards.

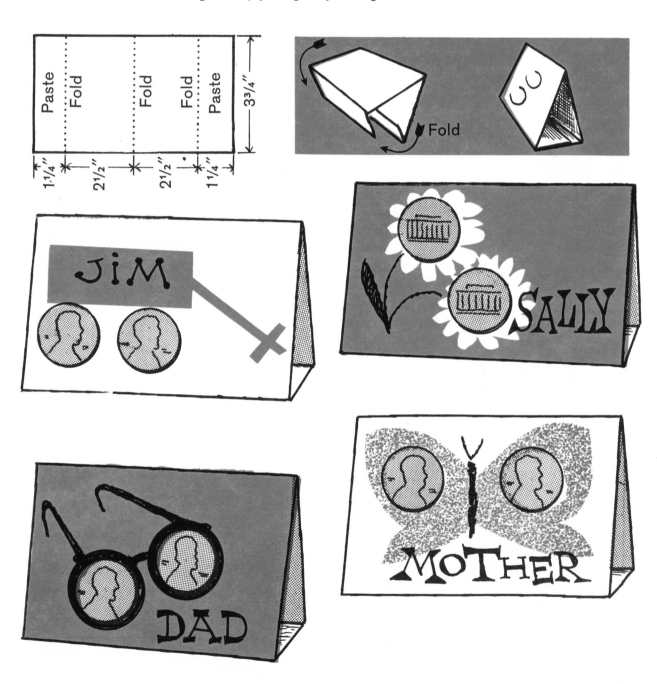

A Hatchet Catch-it

To make a George Washington candy dish, use an empty salt box. Draw area on one side, as shown. Cut out. Next, cut a piece of tinfoil 12″ x 5″. Lay it inside your box and shape it to form an area for holding candies. Cover the box outside with wood-grained, adhesive-backed paper, or paste on brown paper. For the base, cut two strips of cardboard 4½″ x ¾″. Cut the ends at an angle. Make slits in the bottom of the box and slip onto the strips. This will make your hatchet catch-it stand without rolling.

Make the axe from a strip of heavy red paper, 1″ x 3″. Fold in half and glue over a 4″ piece of pipe cleaner or a straw. Cut a slit on the top of your log. Slip in the axe and fill the box with candies.

A Quiet Drum Coaster

Many spray cans come with white, large-size plastic tops about 2¾″ across. These make ideal coasters. Cut three strips of 1½″ red fabric sticky tape 1½″ long to fit the cover. Space evenly around. If the top is not white, alternate with strips of white tape. With a nail, scissors or other sharp object, poke holes in the top center of each red and white area. Thread a large needle with blue yarn, and lace it through the first hole, down to the corner of the tape. Lift the tape a little and catch the yarn under the corner. Press the tape and hold as you go up to the next hole, through, and back down. If the tape doesn't hold at the corners, use glue. The final result will be a fine drum coaster for your glass.

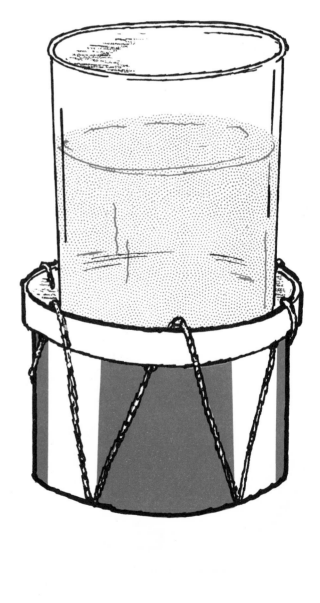

Hare-Brained Game

This party game is fun for any occasion. Get a large piece of brown wrapping paper. Enlarge the squares here to whatever size bunny you need. Paint him white or cut him out of white paper and paste onto the brown. With a felt-tipped pen, draw in the eyes and whiskers. Then hang your bunny on the wall.

Tails are powder puffs that can be bought at the dime store in packages of a dozen. Put a safety pin through the powder puff. Close the pin. Attach a piece of transparent tape through the pin when each guest is ready to try to pin the tail on the bunny. The guest closes his eyes and walks to the wall. When he touches the wall where the bunny is, he sticks down the tape to hold the tail in position. The one getting the cotton tail closest to where it should be wins the prize—perhaps a chocolate bunny.

The Bunny Express

The train engine can be made from cookie, cereal, candy or gift boxes—whatever you can find. The rear cars are plastic or wooden berry boxes. Paint these gay colors and add as many as you like.

You'll need a round salt box for the engine front. Cover it with bright paper. Trace smokestack pattern (next page) on black paper. Cut out and paste together. For position, mark 1″ from the end of the salt box and cut out a ¾″ hole. Insert the smokestack in the hole. Tape, if necessary, to hold in place.

The box for the cab should be about 6″ x 3″ x 4″. A two-quart milk container will also do. (If you use a milk carton, open the top, cut off any excess and fold it down, making a peak.) Cover the cab with bright adhesive-backed plastic. Cut out three windows and glue this box to the round box. Make sure your smokestack stands straight up.

Continued on page 20

18

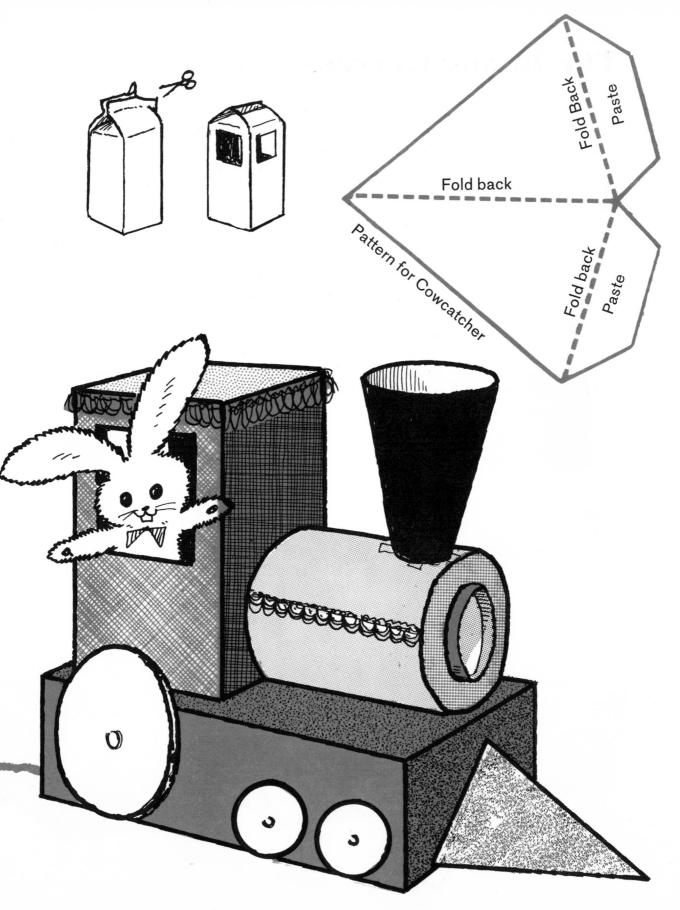

Fold Back

Paste

Fold back

Fold back

Paste

Pattern for Cowcatcher

19

The Bunny Express cont'd

The box for the base should be about 2″ x 10″ x 4″. (Sizes can vary but all the parts should look good together.) Cover it to look like the rest of the engine.

The wheels are various plastic or cardboard tops. The cardboard liners from metal jar tops can be removed to get nice round wheels. Tops from cheese or yogurt containers are also good. Line up the wheels with the bottom of the box. Poke a hole through the wheel and the box. Put a double-pronged paper fastener through and open it inside.

Use a small jar top for the headlight in front of the engine. Glue its flat side to the box. For the cow catcher, trace the pattern on heavy paper. Cut, fold and glue it into position.

To hold your bunny express together, tie a knot in the end of a piece of string. Poke it through the back of the base box (see illustration) and tie on the berry boxes. Assemble the rest of your train as shown.

Ask your mother if she has any scraps of rickrack or other fancy trimmings. Glue these around the cab and box tops for a gay effect. If you have a toy rabbit about 3″ high, let him drive the cab—or use a chocolate bunny. If not, draw a rabbit. Then color, cut out and put him inside. Fill the berry baskets with Easter grass, eggs and candies. Happy Holiday! And enjoy the ride!

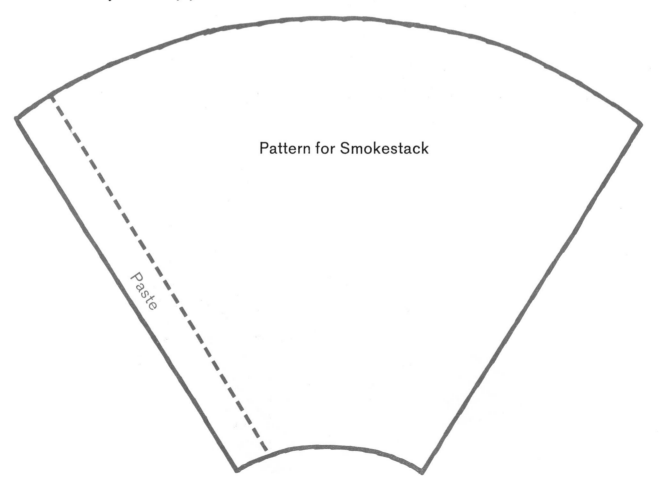

Paste

Pattern for Smokestack

Bonnet Bewitchery

Here is a sunny-as-spring Easter hat for you to make. Turn over a gallon plastic bleach (or other type) jug. Mark off 3″ from the base, and cut. Place on a 9″ paper plate and trace around. Cut out the center of the plate. Tape the crown in place. Pull some paper grass from your Easter basket and form into a strip about 1″ wide. Glue to your hat at the crown edge. When dry, shake off any excess.

Cut strips of tissue or crepe paper 4″ x ½″. Gather in the center and twist a pipe cleaner around tightly. Fold out the paper to make a funny floppy flower. Tuck the stem between the crown and brim; fold back and tape in place.

Easter Whimsies

There are lots of delightful ways to decorate blown or hard-boiled eggs. All sorts of things can be stuck on to make them pretty or amusing. Here are some silly animals done with fabric scraps. (Pretty cotton prints work best.) Trace off the patterns. Then cut the shapes and glue in place.

Rabbit: Cut ears and belt. Cut bits of stale marshmallow. Glue on to make feet and tail, and to help him stand. Draw in his features with a felt-tipped pen.

Rabbit Ear Pattern

Bird Wing Pattern

Beak Pattern

Fold

Chicken and Owl: Glue on wings. Cut beak out of paper. Fold and paste in place. Draw (as shown) under beak. Shape pipe cleaner to make feet and stand. Glue on bottom.

Cat: Cut ears of fabric. Feet are stale marshmallows. Tail is a piece of glued-on yarn.

Mouse: Ears are fabric. Make feet from a pipe cleaner, ends bent forward to look mouse-like. Tail is a 3″ piece of yarn.

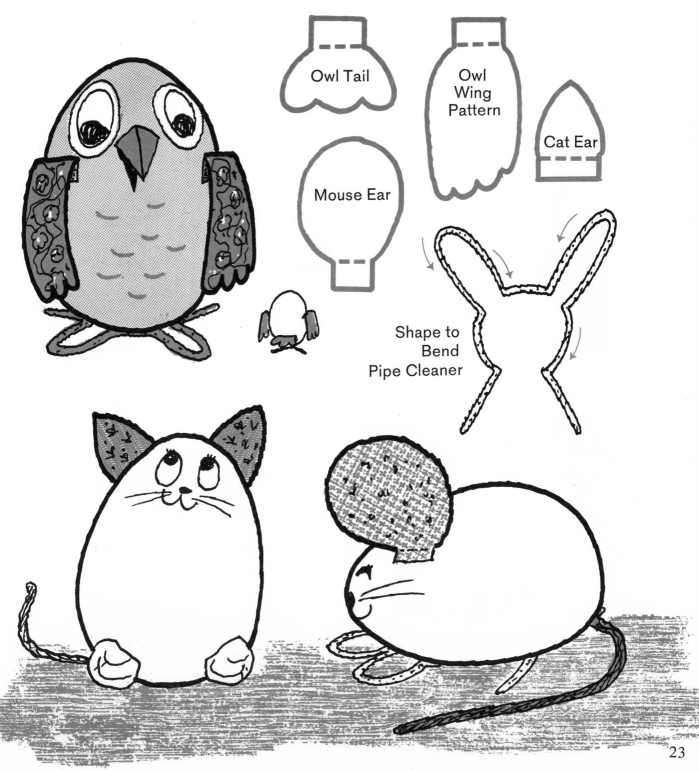

Owl Tail

Owl Wing Pattern

Cat Ear

Mouse Ear

Shape to Bend Pipe Cleaner

Be Sweet to Mother

For Mother's Day, make your own sweet card by simply using a lollipop. Cut a piece of white construction paper 7″ x 10″. Fold it in half. (The size will vary according to the size of your lollipop.) Tape the lollipop, as shown. Use colored, felt-tipped pens to letter your message. Cut some of the words out of old magazines. Use your imagination and humor.

A Pin-up Mother's Day

Make this pretty pin from a homely, molded egg carton. Trace the pattern onto the lid of the carton. Cut it out. Soak, then shape by placing it in a small cup to dry. This curls the petals up. Cut two notches in the bottom of the larger piece and slip in a safety pin, as shown. Paint the larger piece pink. Paint the smaller shape yellow. Paint a piece of narrow spaghetti purple. When dry, break in 2″ pieces.

Paint some purple dots on the pink petals. Paint a crisscross star in the center of the yellow shape. When dry, glue the yellow shape in the middle of the pink piece. Poke the purple spaghetti sticks under the yellow shape, catch them in glue, and let dry throughly. Last, and for a lovely effect, give the entire pin several coats of colorless pearl nail polish.

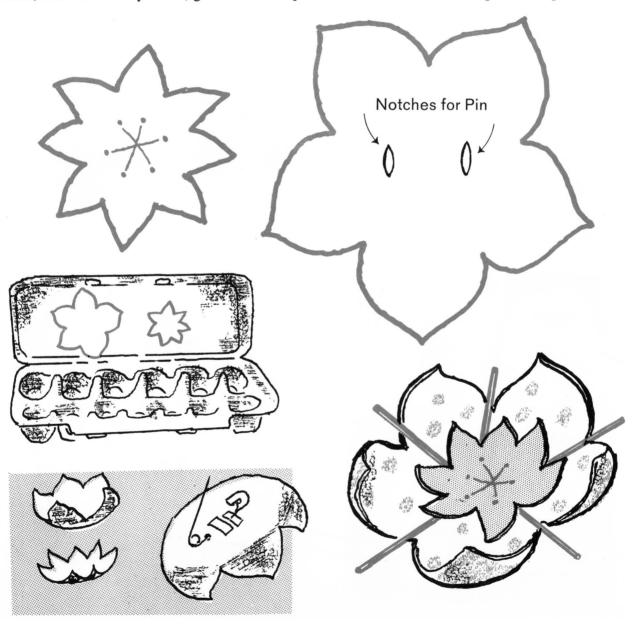

Notches for Pin

A Blooming Bunch

This bunch of flowers also starts as a homely egg carton. Cut around the base of the egg cups and trim in petal shapes. (Figure 1.) Cut out center circle. Cut center dividers from between the cups and trim into four petal shapes. (Figure 2.) They don't have to be exactly even. Now soak until soft. Curve the petals gently back to form a flower shape. Let dry in position. Poke a small hole in the shape. (Figure 2.) Insert into first shape. Glue in place. For the stem, use colored straws. Insert the end of the straw through the small hole, and glue. Make as many flowers as you like. When dry, paint pretty colors.

Place a lump of clay or styrofoam in a small bowl. Find a small natural branch and glue on some paper leaves. Poke this into the clay. Cut the straws different lengths. Poke holes in the clay and insert the straws in an attractive, original arrangement. Mother will be thrilled when you surprise her with this bright table decoration.

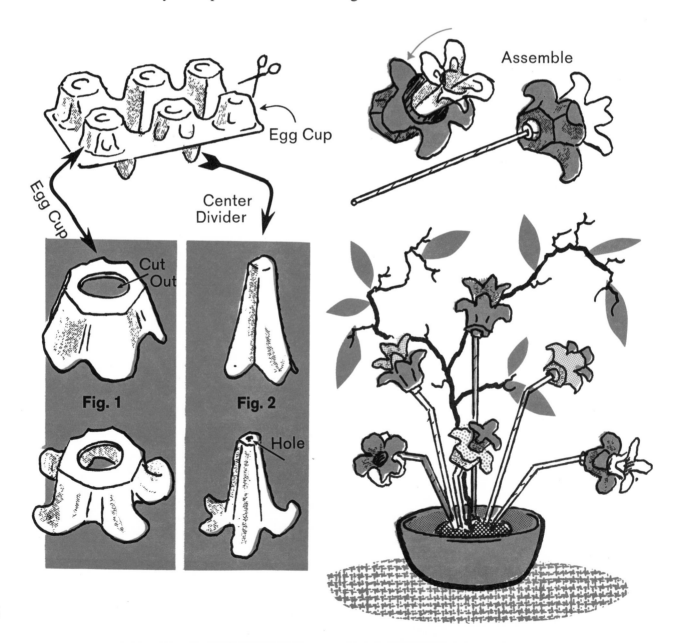

Egg Cup

Egg Cup

Center Divider

Cut Out

Fig. 1

Fig. 2

Hole

Assemble

For Dad—The Space Ace

For a unique Father's Day card, look in old magazines to find a picture of a space capsule. (There are plenty of pictures around these space-age days.) Paste the picture on the outside of folded construction paper to fit it. Either letter in the message or cut words out of old magazines, or combine the two. You'll have fun creating your own Dad's Day card.

OUTSIDE

INSIDE

For MY out of this World DAD Happy Father's Day

A Weighty Matter

To make this Father's Day present, find a smooth attractive rock not more than 3″ to 4″ across. Scrub it clean and let it dry. Decide what kind of picture your father likes and paint the design on the rock with poster paints. When dry, cover with clear nail polish. After this dries, give the underside a coat of polish so the whole rock shines—just like your father's face when he sees his paperweight.

28

Have a Happy Ball

Cut strips of crepe paper about ¾″ wide. They can be many colors or all the same. Buy some small trinkets you think the person you're going to give it to will like. Charms, covered candies, or small toys will do nicely.

Start with the largest item. Take the end of the crepe paper. Wrap it around the item until it is covered. Continue around, forming a ball. Then add another item. When you come to the end of a strip, tape it onto the end of the next one. Continue winding firmly around and around, adding items as you go. Try to keep a ball shape all the time. When finished, tape down the end and paste on a decoration.

To unwind, begin with the decoration. A surprise ball is good for birthdays, when someone is sick, or for any occasion. It combines a present and the fun of unwinding.

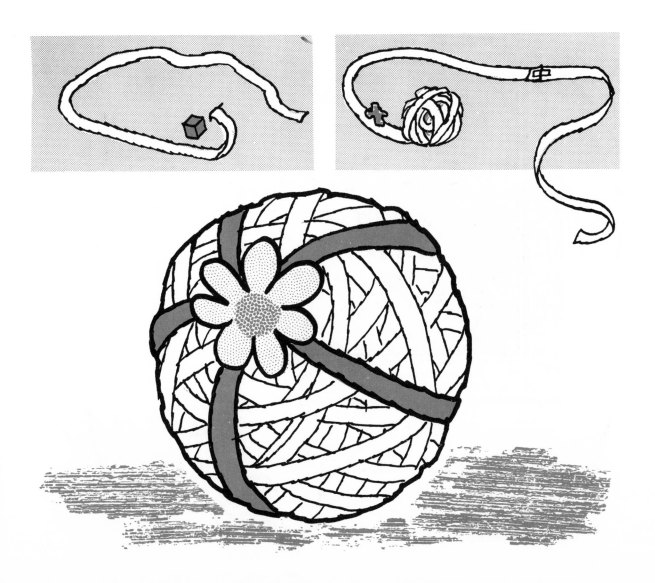

A Pachyderm Party Invitation

To make this original, stand-up birthday party invitation, trace the outline of this elephant onto a shirt board. Cut two outlines for each invitation and staple them together at the top. Next cut a piece of yellow paper 6″ x 3¼″. Fold in half and decorate the edges. Paste over the elephant. Letter your message on one side and put the time, place and date of your party on the other side. Trace off the head decoration. Cut out, fold, and decorate. Paste on the head. Draw eyes and tusks. Make one for each guest you invite.

Fold | **PATTERN**

DATE....
TIME....
PLACE....

Fold

DON'T FORGET COME TO MY PARTY

Know Your Place

For place favors, trace off the tent pattern onto heavy paper. Color in tent scallops and ends. Write on the name of each guest. Poke holes, as shown. Fold as indicated and paste area A onto area B. Fold up ends and paste small tabs inside. Use two lollipops for each. Push sticks through the top holes to the bottom holes. Tape to steady if necessary. Cut a flag shape of bright paper to fit your lollipop and tape it on. For a tasty surprise, fill your circus tent with animal crackers.

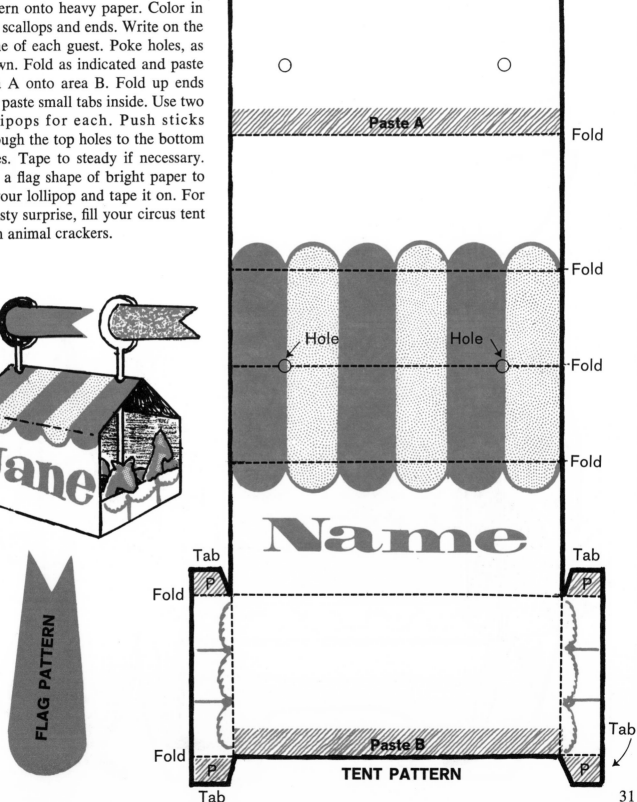

Paste A

Fold

Fold

Hole

Hole

Fold

Fold

Name

Tab

Tab

Fold

P

P

FLAG PATTERN

Paste B

Fold

P

P

Tab

Tab

TENT PATTERN

Jane

31

Jester For the Fun of It

For this birthday party game, use a large piece of paper about 18″ x 36″. Draw a face of a silly clown. Make his eyes about 3″ apart. Cut out the eyes and make sure you can look through easily. Eye holes should be about 1½″ around. Paint your clown face bright colors.

When game time comes, have your mother put up a blanket across a doorway and tape the clown face across it. Choose two teams. One team goes behind the door. One at a time the players step up on a small box or stool and peek through the eye holes. The players on the other team try to guess who it is—just from the eyes! After everyone is guessed, the teams change places. The team with the most correct guesses wins.

Memory Mural

After your birthday, you probably had many cards you hated to throw away. Why not make a memory mural? Cut a piece of sturdy cardboard 7″ x 12″. Cover this panel with light-colored paper. If you got a card with your age number, begin with it. Cut out the animals or pictures from other cards or use the whole card front. If you have a birthday snapshot, include that. A pretty napkin or invitation to your party might also add interest.

Lay them all on the panel. Arrange so they look well together. Then paste down, making a collage. Hang on your bulletin board. Be sure to write on the year. Then each year, make another panel the same size. Taped together, they can stand on your bureau or across your wall, a lovely reminder of all your special days.

"YEAR"

Center of Attraction

This Uncle Sam decoration is made out of two large juice cans and a paper plate.

For the hat, cut a piece of red paper 14″ x 6¾″ and a piece of blue paper 14″ x 1½″. Paste them together on the bottom of the red piece. Paste 1″ vertical white strips above the blue, leaving a 1″ red stripe showing. (See drawing).

For the face, cut a piece of pink paper 14″ x 6¾″. Using the pattern below, cut the nose out of the dark pink or red paper, and paste as shown. Add eyes (½″ dots) and mouth. For the hair, cut several pieces of white yarn 7″ long. Paste 4″ in from both sides of the pink piece. When dry, trim off edges. Tape this piece around one can. Tape the red, white and blue piece around the other can for a hat.

For Uncle Sam's eyebrows, cut a piece of white yarn and glue it back and forth, covering an area about 1½″ x ¾″ over each eye. For chin whiskers, cut 2″ pieces of yarn. Gather at the top and tape on under the mouth. Gather and glue at the bottom, leaving a puff in the middle.

The hat brim is a 7″ paper plate, painted a bright color if it needs it. To assemble, glue the top can over the plate. The face-covered can goes below. Set Uncle Sam on a turned-over saucer or on another small plate.

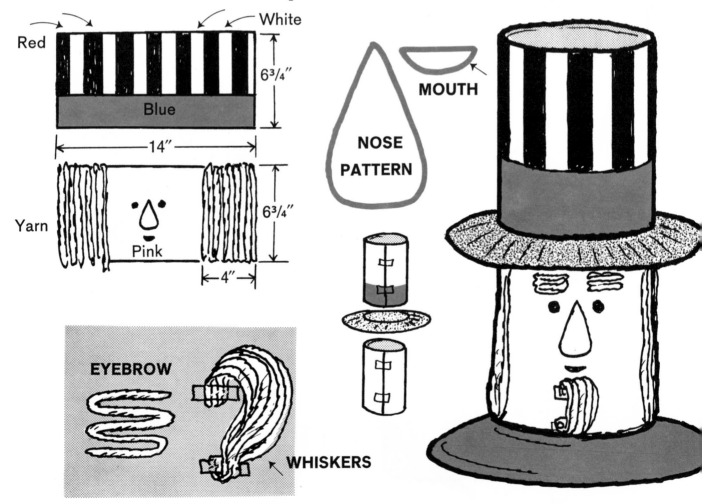

34

A Swinging Swoosher

Use three strips of crepe paper ¾″ by 3 feet long each. Make a red, a white and a blue strip. Glue the ends around an empty spool. Cut a piece of string 18″ long. Slip through the spool hole and tie, as shown. Tie a loop to hold on to.

Swing it in a circle around your head, faster and faster until the streamers make a fine swooshing sound.

A Patriotic Party Popper

To make this popper, use a 4″ piece of cardboard tube. Poke small holes opposite each other about 1½″ from one end. Push a rubber band through and leave a piece sticking out on each side. Hold the ends by a piece of toothpick slipped through the ends outside the tube. Twist the ends until the rubber band is tight inside. Interlock two paper clips. Slip one over the twisted rubber band inside the tube. Cut a circle the diameter of the tube from the kind of plastic top that comes on coffee, cottage cheese or orange drink. Tape this to the end near the rubber band. Reach in from the open end and grasp the paper clip. Pull. Then release suddenly. It should make a "pop!" Finish your firecracker with red paper. Last, tape a 3″ piece of red string to the covered end.

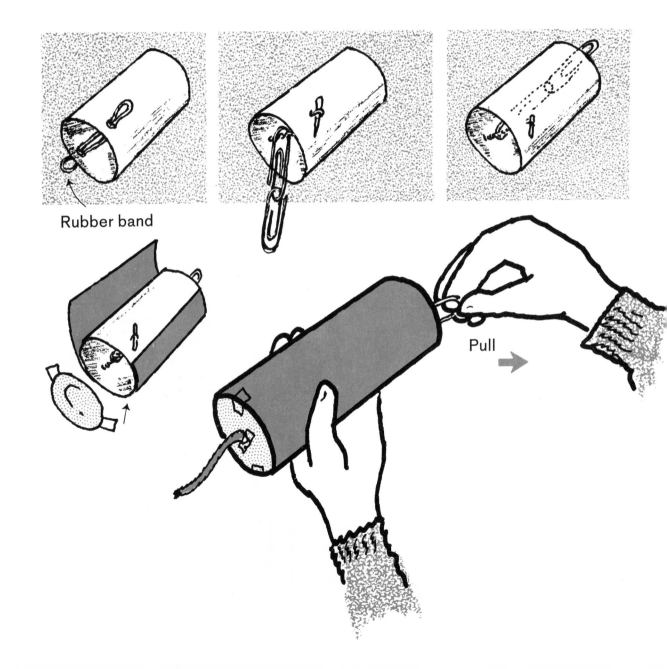

Rubber band

Pull

Seasonal Sorcery

Trace shapes A and B onto heavy paper. Draw all the letters and designs in *exactly* the same places as pictured. Cut out. Fold piece A, as shown. Fold around piece B and paste. (Be very careful not to get any paste on piece B.) When dry, pull B out to the right, and it's *summer*. Show your friends how you can change the seasons. Pull out to the left; suddenly summer turns to *autumn!*

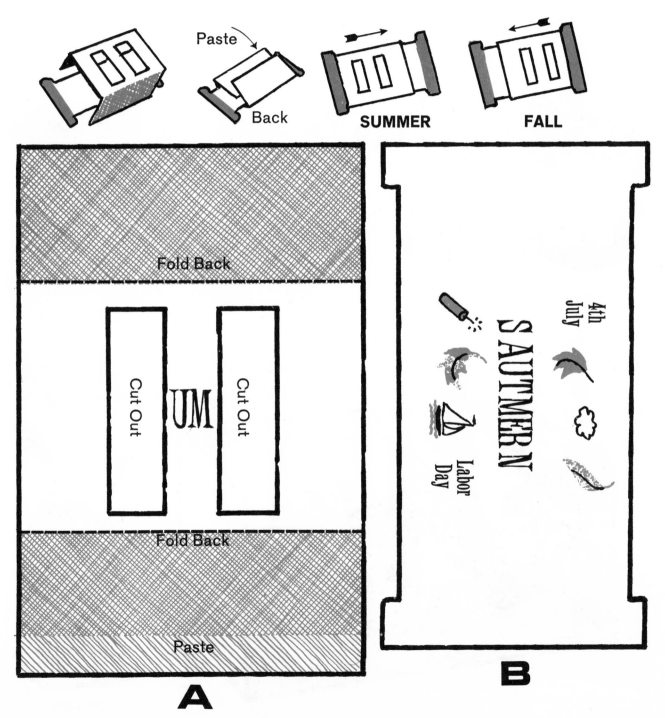

Paste

Back

SUMMER

FALL

Fold Back

Cut Out

UM

Cut Out

Fold Back

Paste

A

4th
July

S AUTMER N

Labor
Day

B

Pretty Crafty-Chris

Remember Columbus Day with a diorama. Start with a box about the size shown. Cut off the top and one side. For the background, cut a piece of blue paper 8″ x 25″. Color halfway up, a blue-green ocean color. Color the water part of the box floor the same color; the island part brown. Trace off one ship shape and draw three ships on the water's edge. Curve your piece around and paste it to the box sides.

Make Columbus from a clip clothespin. For breeches, cut a piece of thin fabric and wrap it around the clothespin near the spring. Glue and tape in place. For arms, wrap around a pipe cleaner ½″ from the top. Cut and fold up ¼″ for hands. Trace his face on pink paper. Cut out and glue in place. For chest armor, crush a small piece of aluminum foil

Pipe Cleaner

SOLDIER

COLUMBUS

Spaghetti

INDIAN

around his middle. Cut his cape from 2″ x 3″ of bright material. Cut slits, and put the arms through. Poke the fabric up under the pipe cleaner in back, and glue. Paint the back and sides of his head black. For his hat, cut a piece of felt ¾″ square. Add a tiny bit of cotton for the feather, and glue to the top of his head. Following the pattern, cut a flag out of fabric. Color with felt-tipped pens and glue to a 6″ piece of spaghetti. Slip this in his hands. Put a toothpick sword in his other hand.

The soldier is made the same way except that his cape has no arm slits—gather it all in back. His flag is half the size. To look like armor, cover his pipe-cleaner arms and the back and sides of his head with aluminum foil. Using the pattern, cut a helmet shape from a disposable aluminum foil plate. Slip it between the clothespin clip. Last add his face.

To make the Indian, cut a skirt piece ¾″ x 2½″. Cut slits and paste around. Cut his feathers from fabric and glue them to his head and spear tip.

Make a stand for each figure from a piece of corrugated cardboard 1¼″ x 2″. Cut slits where the feet touch; push in and glue. To make the background row boat, cut the top of a molded egg carton, as shown. Fold around, tape and shape. Paint the boat brown. Cut silhouettes of black paper, using the pattern. Put a lump of clay in the boat to hold the silhouettes in place. Add the flag.

For a final touch, add a palm tree with paper leaves, and a drinking-straw trunk. Also add green paper grass stuck into a lump of brown clay, and real stones for "boulders." Have as many Indians and soldiers as you like, and arrange them the way you imagine it was.

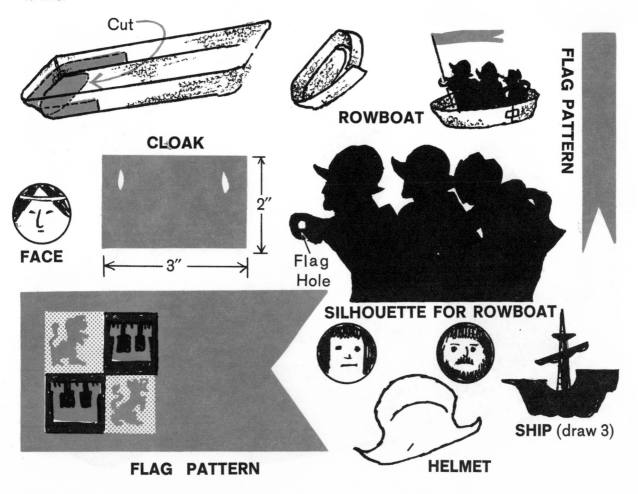

Cut

ROWBOAT

CLOAK

2″

3″

FACE

Flag Hole

FLAG PATTERN

SILHOUETTE FOR ROWBOAT

SHIP (draw 3)

FLAG PATTERN

HELMET

Gong-Ho Halloween

For this gong, use two disposable aluminum foil pie plates the same size. Draw a skull face with a black felt-tipped pen on the back of one plate. Put a handful of gravel or dried peas in the plate. Using clear household cement, put glue all around the plate rims. Glue together, bottom sides out, as shown. Hold with clip clothespins until dry. (Check to see if the glue held firmly all around—there must be *no* open spots or the peas will fall out.) Add more glue wherever necessary, and let dry. Poke a hole in the top and tie on a piece of string about a foot long for a holding loop.

You can also make a jack-o-lantern gong by following the same procedure. This time color the plate with a red felt-tipped pen. Then draw his black grin and eyes.

On Halloween, hold your gong by the string. Jump up and down and hit it with the eraser end of a pencil. Scare as many goblins as you can by the noise.

Edible Witchcraft

Find a fat carrot—1½″ across its widest part is fine. Cut the bottom flat and trim off the top to a blunt point, so you have a piece about 6″ long. Use a piece of toothpick about 1¾″ long for each arm. Make holes on the carrot sides halfway up from the bottom. Push both toothpicks through raisins (as many as needed) and then into the carrot. The face should be just above arm level. To make the eyes and mouth, poke holes and push in whole cloves. For the nose, cut ¼″ off a walnut meat. Stick ½″ piece of toothpick in the nutmeat and push it into the carrot.

For the hat peak, cut a shape out of black paper, using the pattern. Curve around and try on. Overlap until it fits. Tape. Remove and trace around the base on black paper. Draw a circle ½″ larger around this. Cut out the center and around the brim. Slip the brim onto the carrot, stopping above the eyes. Add peak and tape together.

The broom is a twig from a bush or tree (about 3½″). Cut several lengths of black yarn, 1¼″. Tie on the stick, as shown. Push it between the last two arm raisins. Make your witch the same day you'll use her, or keep refrigerated as she'll shrivel!

Her black cat is a prune with a raisin head, paper ears, a yarn tail and toothpick feet.

NOSE

HAT

HAT PEAK PATTERN

Be a Boar

To make this fearsome, frightening boar mask use a 10″ paper plate and a paper cup. Cut the cup as shown. Using the cut piece, trace around it on the paper plate. Cut out a circle ¼″ smaller than your outline. Draw and cut out eyes. Make two breathing holes in the cup. Push the cup through the plate from the back. Tape snugly in place, breathing holes down.

Using a smaller plate, cut as shown. Staple horns to the top (flat side of staple in back). Cut 1″ slits in the sides of the mouth area. Slide in the large tusk end and tape from behind. With felt-tipped pens, color your mask as ugly as you like, with bright stripes and dots. Last, poke holes on each side, add string, and tie around your head.

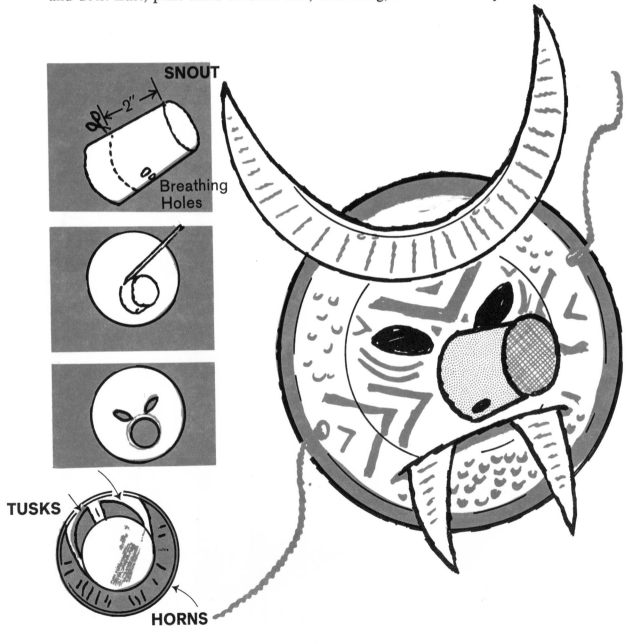

SNOUT

2″

Breathing Holes

TUSKS

HORNS

42

Diabolically Clever

This devil mask is made from a flat molded vegetable or meat carton. Get as large a one as possible—at least 10″ long. Cut off the top edge. Then cut the nose, eyes and mouth. Soak in water. Shape the nose out and curve your mask. When dry, it should remain in shape. Next find a lightweight box that will fit over the back of your head. Cut to size, as shown. On the sides of the box, cut three slits 2″ long and 2″ apart. Cut cardboard tubes in 6″ long pieces. Cut open one side, slip into each slit on the box and turn until in position, making a 3-eared effect.

To make the horns, cut an aluminum foil plate, as shown. Staple the horns in place. Poke holes along the carton side and lace a string in and out of the box section to hold together. Check to see if the mask fits over your head. Cut eyebrows from the remaining rim of the foil plate and glue on. Also glue on black yarn pieces for a beard. Paint as horribly as you please.

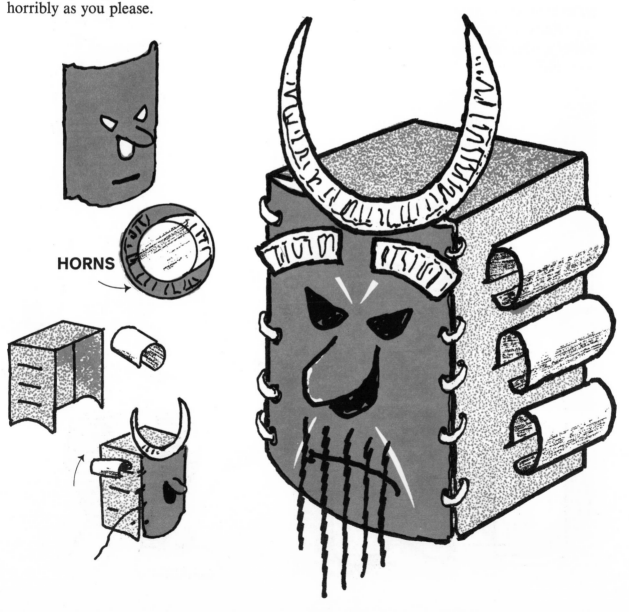

HORNS

Split Personality

This two-faced monster mask is made from a small corrugated box that fits over your head and two molded egg cartons. Try on the box. The corner should be by your nose. Mark eyes and nose holes. Also mark to fit comfortably on your shoulders. Remove, and cut.

For bulging fake eyes, cut out the cup parts of the egg carton. From the section between the egg cups, cut the long nose piece. Cut off the cover of the carton. Trace the size for the eye and nose pieces in position. To complete the false face, cut out the holes. Then slide in the eyes and nose from behind, and tape. Repeat this process for the other face. Then cut out four ear shapes; slide in the slits below the false eyes, and tape. Paint the faces different colors; make the eyes stare. When dry, glue in place on the box, as shown by the dotted line. Bend the ears forward so you can see through the eye holes between the two faces. Add a silly hat on top.

For your costume, use two worn-out shirts of your father's. Measure your arm length. Cut two sleeves off one shirt. Gather the tops and stuff the sleeves with newspaper. Also stuff an old pair of gloves and sew to the sleeve ends. Wear the second shirt and have someone pin on (with safety pins) the two stuffed arms, front and back. Pipe cleaners twisted in your shoelaces make your feet look funny too. Now you are going both ways.

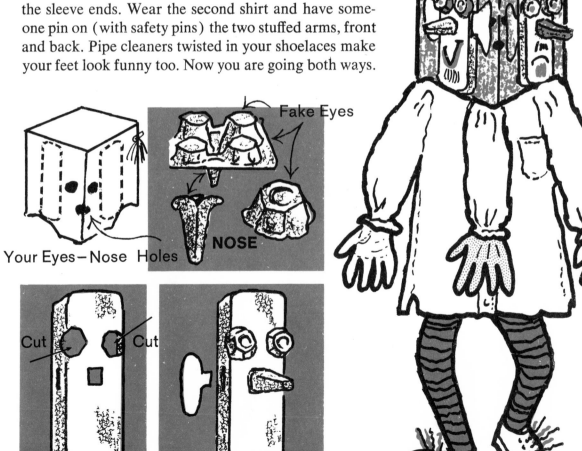

Your Eyes — Nose Holes

Fake Eyes

NOSE

Cut   Cut

Fortunately Yours

Make this fortune broom from an old broom stick, or any 2 ft. stick you might find in your yard.

Use large-size drinking straws—as many as the number of guests you plan to have at your Halloween party, plus a few extra. On a piece of lightweight paper, 1″ x 2½″, write a fortune, such as comes in fortune cookies. Roll up and slip in the end of a straw, leaving ¼″ sticking out. Put one fortune in each straw. Now gather the straws 3″ from the other end and tie tightly onto the stick. Dress as a witch and go around to each guest, who picks his fortune from the broom.

Or use your broom for a game of charades. Instead of a fortune, write on the paper "Be a lion tamer," or whatever you think might be most fun.

A Bat-Mobile

This Halloween decoration begins with two wire coat hangers. Bend the bat hanger, as shown. Trace around the hanger for the basic shape of bat wings. Cut two pairs of wings with scalloped edges out of black paper. Paste on bat head, a circle 2½″ in diameter; add ears.

Bend the witch hanger sides down slightly. Trace off this shape and cut two triangles of black paper for the dress. Draw two 2½″ circles on orange paper. Cut as shown to make the nose. Draw eyes and mouth; add yarn hair. Make your witch's hat from a triangle 3″ at the base and 4″ high, cut from black paper. Add a brim. Make two triangle hats.

For the broom, find a thin stick about 22″ long; add 3″ strips of black paper at one end. Tape in position on the witch hanger. To assemble, place the dress, face and hat in place and paste the two sides together, sandwiching the hanger. Tape along the edges if necessary to hold the hanger in place. When dry, tie a 4″ piece of thread to the top of the hat. Then tie your witch to the right side of the bat hanger.

For the cat, cut two 6″ circles. Cut two black shapes 4″ x 2½″. Add ears and eyes to make the head. Glue a 6″ piece of yarn between the circles for the tail. Glue on the head and tie on a 6″ piece of thread at the top. The cat ties to the left of the bat hanger.

Tie a hanging thread to the top of the bat hanger. Move the cat and witch back and forth until they balance. Then tape the threads. Now paste the two bat pieces together over the hanger, and hang up your mobile.

BAT

WITCH

4″

3″

Cut
Out

CAT

46

Horn of Plenty-Crafty

A cornucopia, symbol of harvest abundance, can be made from an empty gallon plastic (bleach) bottle. Mark 1″ below where the handle joins the bottle. On the opposite side, mark where the seam hits the bottle base. Then draw a curved line up around the bottle, as shown, to connect your marks. Cut along this line. Cut off the handle flush with the sides.

Take a piece of aluminum foil at least 12″ square. Crush around and together, making a tube shape about 9″ long and 1½″ thick. Slip one end over the cap of the bottle and around into the hole where the top of the handle was. Tuck down inside, and tape edges. Now crinkle the foil piece around and up until it resembles the end of a real cornucopia. With colored adhesive-backed paper, cover the outside of the bottle and over the handle holes and where the taped edge shows. Punch a tiny hole in each side at the base and insert a toothpick. This keeps your cornucopia from rolling. Set your horn of plenty on a platter, and fill it with fruits, vegetables and nuts.

Toothpicks

47

Let's Talk Turkey

This fine turkey is made from a nice fat pine cone and a brown cardboard tube. Find a pine cone about 3″ long. (If smaller, make the other pieces smaller too.) Cut the wings, neck and base from the tube. The neck should be about 1¼″ around. Cut a notch in the top and cut notches in the base. Fold the wings, as shown. Fit all these pieces into the pine cone. Adjust the notches to fit your cone—each one is different. Then glue. On lightweight cardboard, trace around the widest part of your cone. Add 1″ outside and ½″ inside, and cut the tail shape as shown.

Tape the base to a piece of cardboard 3″ x 4¼″. Push the cone into the base until firm; add glue to hold. Then glue on the tail.

The head is a small Brazil nut. Glue and tape to the end of the neck piece. When dry, add a 2″ twist of red crepe paper for the wattle. For a finishing touch, also add a little green Easter grass around the base.

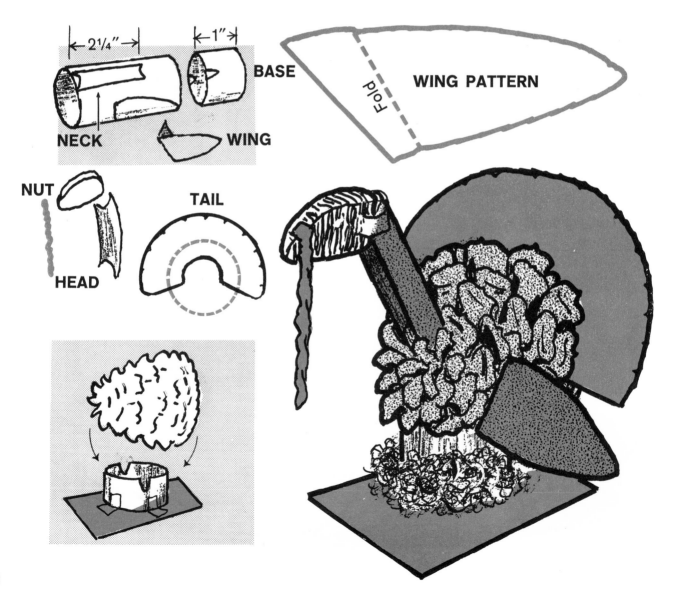

Lucky Pendant

Here is something special you can make from that turkey or chicken wishbone.

When the wishbone is thoroughly dry, paint it white. Poke a hole in the top flat part of the wishbone. Find a small-size plastic top—like the top on a bullion-cube can—or cut a piece from a larger plastic top. Trim the rim to fit around your wishbone.

Glue the wishbone to the plastic with household cement. When dry, give several coats of frosted natural nail polish. When that is dry, add a tiny jeweled button, or sequins, or some old pearls from a necklace that broke. Add trim of whatever pretty trickets you find around the house that you have permission to use. Now you have a pendant that can be worn on a chain and is a lovely piece of jewelry to give or keep.

A Nutty Idea

Make this candle holder from an empty tuna fish can and 3 walnut shell halves. Position the shells on the base of the can. Saturate a piece of cotton with white glue and nest around each shell base. Also glue the shell tips, which should touch in the center. Then glue on 3 almond nutshells between, for decoration. Glue a filbert nut in the center, on top of the walnuts, to look like a little knob. Break thin spaghetti into 1½″ pieces and glue around the sides of the can about ⅛″ apart. When dry, spray the can and shells with gold paint.

Melt some candle wax into each nutshell. While still warm, place a Hanukah or a large birthday-size candle into each shell. Set on a turned-over saucer to complete your decoration.

Re-print Performance

Print your own Christmas cards. First, cut a piece from the side of a corrugated box about 5″ x 8″. Then trace a tree shape on the cardboard, making sure the corrugations are horizontal, as shown. With a knife, cut along the shape and pull off just the top layer of paper, leaving the corrugated ridges showing in the middle.

Cut a piece of typewriter paper in half. Spread red poster paint over the corrugations and around the tree. Lay the paper over while the paint is still wet, and press down. You should get a print like the one shown. When dry, trim neatly to 3½″ x 6″. Mount your print on a piece of heavy green paper, 4½″ x 6½″. Write on your Christmas message and stick on some stationery stars. Make as many prints as you'll need to send cards to all your friends.

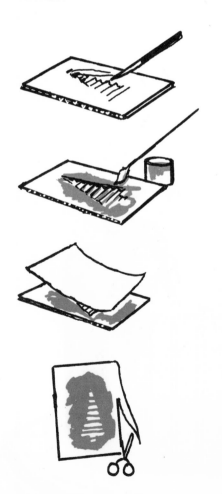

A Toothsome Card

Make this for a special friend. Start with a small wrapped candy cane. Cut a piece of heavy green paper and fold it in half. The paper should be big enough so there is plenty of room all around your cane. Tape the candy cane in position. Trace off the horse's head, making sure it fits over the curved end of your cane. (If not, enlarge where necessary.) Trace onto red paper. Draw on the features. Glue on bits of yarn for the mane. Glue around the edges only and stick on over the candy cane, to look like a hobby horse.

Inside the card, write your happy holiday message.

It's the Berries

Plastic berry baskets can be turned into pretty tree decorations. Baskets come in various patterns. If yours has a crisscross bottom, cut this out and discard the sides. Or, if yours has squares on the bottom, it probably has decorative sides. In this case, cut out and glue the two sides together with household cement, as shown. Trim around the edges till it looks like a snowflake. Take some gold or silver gift-wrapping cord or narrow ribbon and weave it in and out of the holes in a pretty pattern. Using cement, attach sequins on the tips and in the center. With cord, make a loop. Now it will hang merrily on your tree.

Glue

53

Angel of Joy

Use a large plastic detergent bottle that has this basic shape. Clean and dry. For the wings, make cuts on one side of the bottle, as shown by the colored line. Be careful to leave the center between the wings uncut. Fold out the wings and hold them together with a clip clothespin while you work on the figure.

For the arms, poke holes in the shoulders and push a 6″ pipe cleaner into each side. Reach inside the back opening and twist the ends together, making the arms one unit. For the skirt, cut a piece of gay fabric in the size shown. Glue with household cement around her waistline, across the holes in the back and meeting in the center front. Cut two sleeves from fabric, 4″ x 2″. Fold in half and glue or sew the edges together. Slip over the arms, and glue to her shoulder top.

Cut a strip of contrasting fabric or felt 1½″ x 30″. Place the center of the fabric

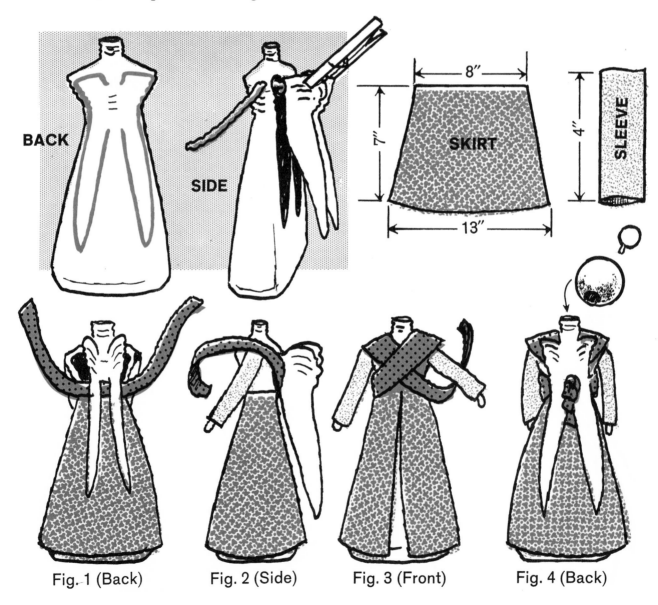

BACK

SIDE

8″

7″

SKIRT

13″

4″

SLEEVE

Fig. 1 (Back)   Fig. 2 (Side)   Fig. 3 (Front)   Fig. 4 (Back)

piece in the center back, beneath the wings (fig. 1). Bring up over her shoulders (fig. 2). Crisscross in front and under the arms (fig. 3), and around the back. Tuck under her wings and tie at center back (fig. 4). Put a bit of glue at the sides of the neck so the material won't slip out of place.

For your angel's head, get a 2″ styrofoam ball. Carve out the base to fit over the neck of your bottle. For her halo, use a curtain ring or loop of wire 1½″ in diameter. Poke into the styrofoam, and glue. Trace eyes and cut out of black paper; the mouth is of red paper. Glue in place. Wind pieces of yarn around for her hair, with small dabs of glue to hold where necessary. Arrange hair to hang down about 3½″ in back. Braid or tie it with a pretty cord. Place your angel's head on her neck, and glue. Her hair should hang down between her wings.

Add some decorative edging around the neck and along the skirt front if desired. Shape her arms around and fold up the ends a little so your angel can hold a tiny ornament or little pine cone between her hands.

BACK

Yule Link

The basis for this lovely chain is lightweight cardboard tubes from inside wax paper or towels. Cover one tube with a scrap of gift-wrapping paper—pretty foil if you have it. Cut in ¾″ wide pieces. Cut another tube down one side; then cut in ¾″ pieces. Slip these between each of the colored foil circles. Tape closed to make the chain. Cut strips of aluminum foil and crush them around the taped links, turning them so that each circle is completely covered.

Make as long a chain as you like, and use it for a wall decoration or for trimming your tree.

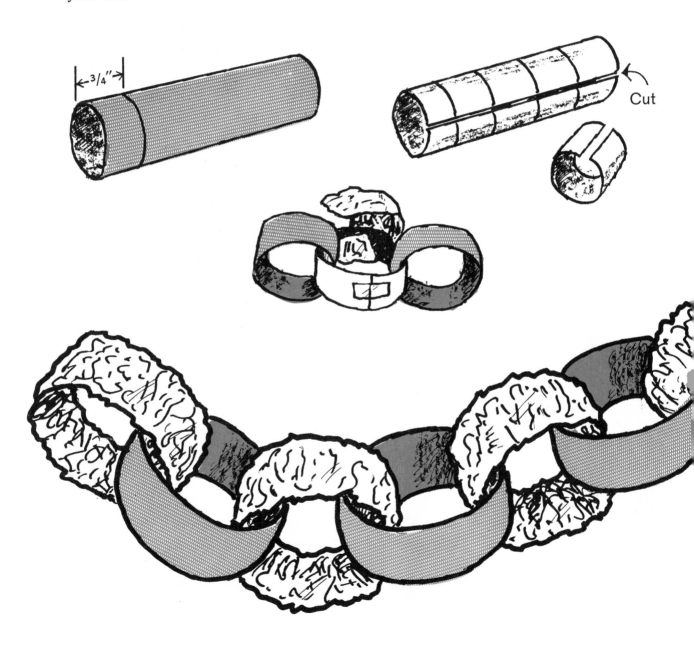

Tag—You're It

These bright shiny tags are made of colored paper and disposable aluminum foil plates or pans. Trace the design and transfer it to the flat part of the plate. Cut out the shape. Lay it on several layers of folded newspaper. With an old dried-up ball-point pen, draw on outlines of stars, etc. Press hard to form ridges. Work some lines from the back to give an embossed look. Color in some areas with brightly colored felt-tipped pens. On colored paper, draw around your outline; add ⅛″ and cut out. Glue the foil piece to the paper with household cement. This gives it a colored border. Punch a hole in the top with a paper punch. Write "To . . . From . . ." on the paper side. Turn over and glue on sequins for tree balls and Santa's nose. Last, add string. Make other similar tags, using your own designs.

Back

Wrap-up Fantastix

Package wrapping can be fun if you use your imagination. Here are a few ideas to get you started.

Make a medium-size package look like a book. Wrap in plain paper. Cut corner triangles of gold paper. Cut a bookmark shape of bright color paper. Tape on in back, fold around, and paste down in place. Print on receiver's name or initials.

Make a wide flat box look like a picture. Paste the background color on the top of your box. Cut the frame from wood-grained adhesive-backed paper. Angle the corners to make it look like a frame. Cut a half circle pink face. Cut a crown from corrugated cardboard. Draw eyes, glue on drinking straws for whiskers and use sequins for the crown tips. Add a final festive touch by gluing a pretty bow on top (which was the box side).

For a smiling Santa present, wrap a box in red paper. Glue on a black belt in his middle. White cotton glued on makes beard, eyebrows, and buttons. Cut out his arms, and tape on. Draw eyes. To make Santa's hat, cover a paper cup with red paper. Tape it to the top. Cut out red triangle. Tape this to the cup, and add a cotton ball at the end.

For the stalwart soldier, draw a face on paper and paste it around a salt (or other round) box. Add a feather. Cover the top of your package in red; the lower half in blue. Glue the salt box on top. Cut feet and arms, and tape in place. Add gold paper stripes, epaulettes and buttons.

Glue cards in their hands saying "To . . . From . . ."

Hang Them Both

Jar and can tops make this lovely wall decoration. Plastic ones are best, but metal ones with rims will do nicely.

Use old Christmas cards or pictures from old magazines, the right size for the tops you have. Trace around the jar top and cut out the picture. Cut an edging from a paper doily, or pleat a ribbon around the edge, as shown, and glue on. Glue your picture over this. Make three.

Cut three circles of lightweight cardboard. Take a piece of wide ribbon and place the three decorations you've done on it, spaced neatly. Trim the bottom of the ribbon and allow for a small fold at the top. Turn your unit over and glue the circles to each cap, with the ribbon sandwiched between. Hang when dry.

This wreath is made of ten pint-size milk cartons. (Ask friends to save them for you from their school lunches if you don't have enough around the house.) Cut each carton as shown. Cut a cardboard circle 10″ across and 1″ wide. Arrange the cartons around it, and mark the places.

For the candle, use a 4″ paper tube. Trace around it on the bottom of one carton. Cut a hole and push in the tube. Tape below if necessary. Paste red crepe paper on the tube, leaving about 2″ above. Twist on top and trim off any excess to get a flame shape. Dab on a bit of yellow paint at the flame end.

Now staple the back edge of each box in position onto the ring. Paint green. You may have to mix a little soap with the paint to make it stick. Poke two holes in the top carton and put in a string. Hang from any door or window, wherever your wreath will give the most cheer.

Front   Side

Back

Dad Knows His Place

Make this just-for-you gift for your father from an old envelope that has a window in it. Cut the envelope across so there is about the same amount of space above the window as below. Cut a piece of bright paper, big enough to go behind the window. On this paper, make an arrangement of dried weeds or flowers. Glue them in place. When dry, slide them into the envelope behind the window so your decoration shows through. Glue in place, around the window.

Tape along the open edge with a piece of colorful, sticky tape. Tape the other edge to match. Decorate and color. Be sure to put on your father's initials to make it personal.

Hanging Niche for Mother

This is made from a large-size plastic detergent bottle. Cut as shown. Maybe your father, with a sharp knife, can help you get the cut just right. Also, he can use a nail or other sharp object to punch a hole in the top. Locate this hole by folding the sides at the top and overlapping them to form a roof on the niche. Make a hole through both and push a pipe cleaner through these holes, around the back and underneath. This holds it together. Trace around the bottom, and cut a piece of cardboard slightly smaller. Fit inside the bottle for a base. Glue in place, and paint inside. Glue narrow lace around the opening and up around the peak. Spray the outside with gold paint or color with a felt-tipped marker. Punch a hole in the back at the top; add string for hanging.

Mother can put her favorite figurine inside this lovely niche or maybe you'll want to buy one for her.

For Small Fry

Nesting cans are like building blocks. They can be fitted inside each other or turned over and piled up. To make this gift, collect cans for several weeks. Have your mother, as she opens them, make sure there are no rough edges anywhere. Save all sorts of cans from the big fruit-drink ones to the smallest frozen-juice or bullion-cube ones. Some (coffee, for instance) will have snap-on plastic tops, which can add to the fun.

Cover each can with adhesive-backed paper. If you don't have any scraps around, you can buy it in the hardware or dime store. It comes in bright nursery patterns sure to please a baby. Measure around each can with a tape measure, adding ½″ for an overlap. Then measure the height. Mark. Cut out, peel off the backing, and stick the paper onto the can. Cover all the cans you've decided to use. Cut out pictures or alphabet letters and stick one on top of each can with household cement. Finish all the cans similarly.

Now show your baby sister or brother how to stack and play.

64

It's About Time

Now that we're at the end of this year, it's time to think about making a colorful mosaic calendar for *next* year. Many companies give away calendars with advertising on them, or you can buy an inexpensive calendar in a dime store.

Cut out the months' section of the calendar you're going to use, and decide what size page you'll need to have room for it, a picture and a mosaic border. Cut a sheet out of heavy gray paper or shirtboard and mount the calendar section on it. Plan a picture for each month, such as the January picture we've shown.

Look around among the holiday wrappings, trims and cards that are about to be thrown out. Any interesting or attractive small scrap will do. You can probably find bright colors, gold and silver (on Christmas cards) and gay foils. Cut into ¼″ squares and triangles. Arrange your mosaic picture. Trim pieces as needed and paste down. Make a colorful mosaic border for each month. When you've done the whole year, punch two holes on the top, put ribbon through, and hang. Happy New Year!

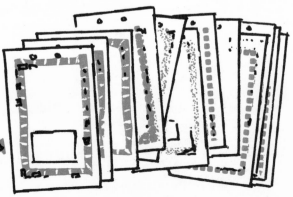